KU-688-373

OVER THE HEDGE

Popcorn
ELT
Readers

C 03 0248933

Meet ...
everyone from
OVER THE HEDGE
DreamWorks

I'm Ozzie.
I'm an opossum.

I'm Penny. I'm a porcupine.

I'm Verne!
I'm a tortoise.

I'm Hammy!
I'm a red squirrel.

I'm Stella.
I'm a skunk.

I'm Gladys.
I live in a new house next to the forest. The houses have gardens and big hedges.

I'm The Verminator.
I don't like animals!

I'm RJ. I'm a raccoon and I love food!

I'm Vincent the bear.
Bears love food too!

Before you read ...
What do you think?
Do the forest animals like the new houses?

New Words

What do these new words mean? Ask your teacher or use your dictionary.

forest

This is a big **forest**.

find

I can't **find** my shoe!

frightened

The boy is **frightened**.

food

There's a lot of **food**.

hedge

There is a tall **hedge** in the garden.

push

She's **pushing** her brother.

wake up

She **wakes up** at seven o'clock.

spring

I like **spring**!

winter

It's cold in **winter**!

'Yum!'

Yum!

take back

I'm **taking** it **back**.

What does the title *Over the Hedge* mean? Ask your teacher.

CHAPTER ONE
Vincent's food

'Wow! Look at that food!' says RJ.
RJ loves food. But there's a problem.
It's Vincent's food.
'Be very quiet!' thinks RJ.

RJ has Vincent's food.

'One more bag …' thinks RJ.

But Vincent wakes up. He is angry.

'That's MY food!' he shouts.

RJ is frightened. He pushes the food into a road. CRASH! There is no more food.

'Find more food for me!' says Vincent. 'You have one week.'

CHAPTER TWO
Spring

'Wake up, everyone!' Verne laughs. 'It's spring!'

The forest animals come out.

'I'm hungry,' says Stella.

'Me too,' says Hammy. 'Let's find some food in the forest!'

Hammy runs to the forest.

'Oh no!' he shouts. 'Come and look at this!'

There is a very big hedge in front of the animals.

'Where's the forest?' asks Verne.

'Now we can't find food for the winter,' says Hammy.

RJ is in the forest. He sees the animals. The animals are good at finding food. And RJ wants a lot of food for Vincent …

'Hi, I'm RJ,' he says. 'Come over the hedge with me. We can find food in the gardens.'

'We don't want to go,' says Verne. 'We're OK here.'

'But there's a lot of food in the gardens,' says RJ.

'I want to go,' says Ozzie.

'Me too,' says Penny.

'Let's go!' says RJ.

CHAPTER THREE
Over the hedge

The animals go over the hedge.

'Wow! Look at this!' says Stella.

'Yum! I love this food!' says Ozzie.

The animals go to the gardens again and again. They eat new food. They play new games.

'We have a lot of food now!' laughs RJ.

Gladys doesn't like the animals in her garden.
The Verminator comes to her house.
'Can you find the animals?' asks Gladys.

Verne is frightened of the Verminator.
He takes the food back to the gardens.

'Oh no!' says RJ. 'Why?'

'It's not your food,' says Verne.

But the animals are angry with Verne. 'RJ is
a good friend,' they say. 'But you are not.'

That night RJ can't sleep. He thinks about Vincent.

'Now I have one day,' says RJ. 'How can I find the food?'

In the morning, Verne is sad.
'I'm sorry, RJ!' he says.
'It's OK,' says RJ. 'We can find more food.
Gladys has a lot of food in her house!'
'OK!' says Verne. 'Let's go!'

CHAPTER FOUR
Into the house

It is night and Gladys is sleeping. The animals are very quiet. They go into the house.

'Look at this food!' shouts RJ. 'Yum!'

The animals are happy. They have a lot of food.

'Quick!' says Verne. 'It's morning!'

'One more bag ...' says RJ.

But Gladys wakes up and sees the animals.
'AAAH! Stop the animals!' she shouts.

RJ runs away with the food. He gives the food to Vincent.

'Very good, RJ!' says Vincent. 'And no more forest animals! Look!'

Oh no! The Verminator has the animals. 'We're sorry,' the animals say to Verne. 'RJ is not a good friend.'

But RJ is sad.

'The animals are my friends,' he thinks.

He pushes the food into the road ... in front of the Verminator's car.

CRASH!

'Quick!' shouts RJ. 'Run!'

The animals run away from the Verminator
... away from Vincent ... away from the
houses ... and over the hedge.

'It's good to be home,' says RJ.
'Let's find some food in the forest!'
laughs Verne.

THE END

ANIMALS IN THE CITY

People live in cities ... but many animals live there too.

Foxes

Foxes live in many cities in the UK. Some people love them and put food in their gardens. But some people are frightened of the foxes.

fox

raccoon

🌙 Night animals

Many city animals go out at night. In North America there are a lot of raccoons. They eat pet food or food from bins. You can see opossums and skunks at night too.

parakeet

A new home

Some pets run away from their homes. Tortoises, snakes and parakeets sometimes go into gardens and people can't find them. You can now find a lot of parakeets in parks in London and Madrid.

Zzzzz ...

In spring, animals find food. Then in winter, many animals sleep a lot. They sometimes wake up to eat some of the food.

mouse

★ What animals live in towns and cities in your country? ★

What do these words mean? Find out.

people   city   pet
bin   snake

PHOTOCOPIABLE

After you read

1 Put the sentences in order. Write 1–7.

a) RJ talks to the animals. ☐

b) The animals are angry with Verne. ☐

c) The animals eat new food. ☐

d) The animals wake up. 1

e) The animals have a lot of food. ☐

f) The animals see the hedge. ☐

g) Verne takes the food back. ☐

2 Yes or no? Read and circle.

a) Do the animals live in the forest? **Yes** No

b) Is the hedge new? **Yes No**

c) Does the Verminator like animals? **Yes No**

d) Does RJ love food? **Yes No**

e) Does Gladys like the animals in her garden? **Yes No**

f) Is there a lot of food in her house? **Yes No**

Where's the popcorn?
Look in your book.
Can you find it?

Puzzle time!

1 Find six verbs from the story.

A	L	E	F	P	X
W	A	K	E	U	P
R	U	B	E	S	U
R	G	T	Y	H	P
U	H	I	G	O	M
N	S	F	I	K	D
S	R	A	V	O	G
S	L	E	E	P	V

2 Answer the questions.

a) Who finds some food? ....

b) Who finds no food? ....

3 What animals are these?

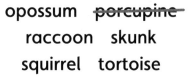

opossum   ~~porcupine~~
raccoon   skunk
squirrel   tortoise

a porcupine

c

b

d

f

e

4 Circle the right word.

a) RJ has Vincent's food. Vincent is
(angry) / **happy** / **frightened**.

b) It's spring. The forest animals are
hungry / **angry** / **frightened**.

c) Verne sees the Verminator. He is
frightened / **angry** / **happy**.

d) The Verminator has the animals. RJ is
happy / **frightened** / **sad**.

Imagine...

1 Work in groups of six. Act out the scene.

Verne: Wake up, everyone! It's spring!

Stella: I'm hungry.

Hammy: Me too. Let's find some food in the forest!

Oh no! Come and look at this!

Verne: Where's the forest?

Hammy: Now we can't find food for the winter.

RJ: Hi, I'm RJ. Come over the hedge with me. We can find food in the gardens.

Verne: We don't want to go. We're OK here.

Ozzie: I want to go.

Penny: Me too.

RJ: Let's go!

Chant

1 🎧 T 8 Listen and read.

Let's go over the hedge

Are you hungry?
Very hungry?
Let's go over the hedge.
Into the gardens.
Find the food.
Quick, quick, quick!

Shhh! Be quiet!
Gladys is coming!

Are you frightened?
Very frightened?
Let's go over the hedge.
Back to the forest.
Eat the food.
Yum, yum, yum!

2 🎧 T 9 Say the chant.